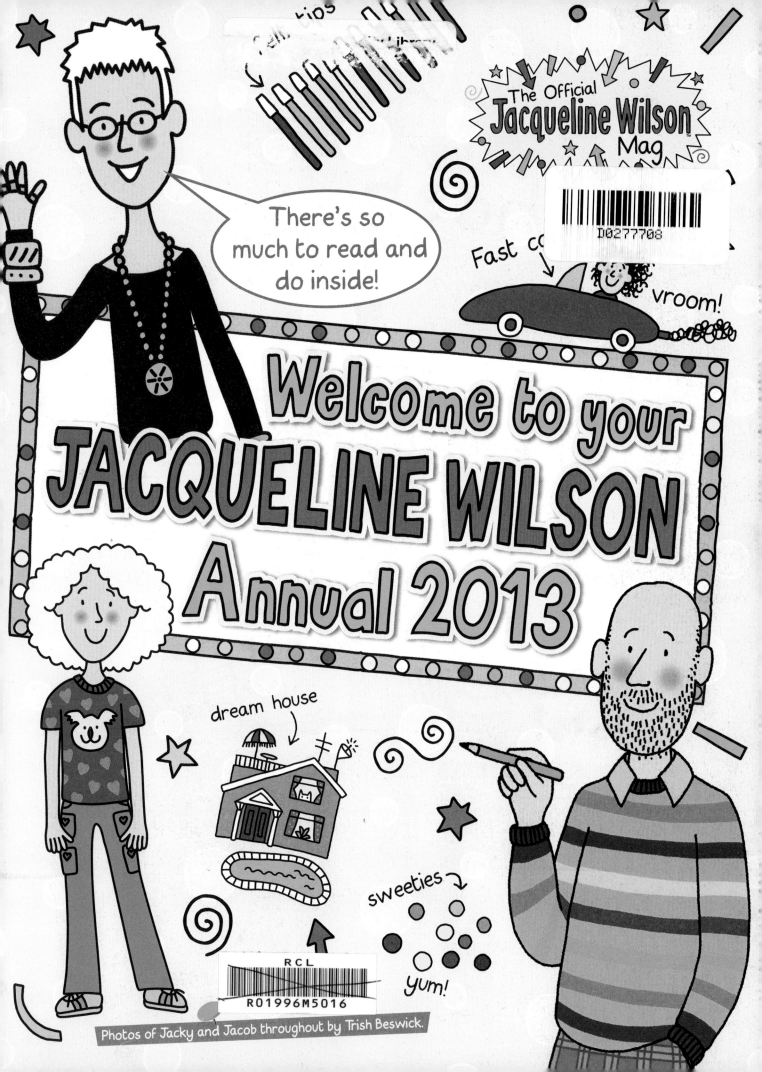

The Official Jacqueline Wilson Mag

There's so much to read and do inside!

Fast co... vroom!

Welcome to your JACQUELINE WILSON Annual 2013

dream house

sweeties
yum!

RCL
R01996M5016

Photos of Jacky and Jacob throughout by Trish Beswick.

All About Me!
This JW Annual belongs to
Phoebe

My favourites!

Colour
Turqiose

felt tips

Animal
Dog,
Red Panda,
horse t cat

Tasty Treat
Choco-
late!

JW Book
Emerald
star

Choose your favourite season

☐ **Winter**   ☐ **Spring**   ☐ **Summer**   ☐ **Autumn**

I still couldn't get used to coming out of school and walking to the Bradshaw Estate. Up until Easter, Mum was always waiting in the car to pick me up and drive me home to Ladywell Crescent. But now everything was changed. We didn't have a car anymore for a start. And Mum was working full-time in a care home to make some money to pay off our debts. And we didn't live in our lovely big house in Ladywell Crescent because it had been taken away from us. We had a new home now: a two-bedroomed top floor flat in the Bradshaw Estate.

It was so weird. For years Mum always said, 'You watch out for the kids from the Bradshaw Estate, our Julie. You know what *they're* like.'

Yet now *I* was one of these scary kids. There was nothing remotely scary about me, worse luck. I'm small for my age, with blue eyes and rosy cheeks, and Mum still ties my hair in two silly bunches and keeps them in place with satin ribbons. She dresses me like a six-year-old too. It's so embarrassing. I got teased a bit when I lived in Ladywell Crescent. You can imagine what it's like for me now.

I do my best to camouflage myself. The moment I step out of the lift I yank my hair free of the ribbons and mess it up a bit and I hitch my cardi sleeves above my elbows and do the buttons up wrongly. I roll down my prim little white socks and scuff my polished sandals. I don't think all this really *works* but I'm desperate.

I walk very, very slowly towards the estate, hoping all the kids who live there have already run ahead. I especially hope Sophie Wallace isn't around. Sophie is the scariest girl ever. Even the boys in the top form at school are scared of Sophie. She's big and tough and she swears and she spits and she'll fight anyone. She once got picked on by a bunch of big lads after a football match and she head-butted one and broke his nose!

I bumped into her the very first day we moved into our new flat. I was taking all our flattened cardboard moving boxes downstairs in the lift and when I stepped out, there was Sophie.

I was so scared I practically wet myself.

'What on earth are *you* doing here, Julie Lyons?' she said.

'I live here,' I mumbled.

'No, you don't, you live up Ladywell with all the posh nobs,' said Sophie.

'Well, I don't live there anymore. I live here,' I said.

'*What?*' said Sophie. She shook her head, wrinkling her nose. Then she grinned. 'So what's happened then? Did your dad lose his job? Did he get into debt? Did you get kicked out of your house?'

She was right on all counts but I wasn't going to tell her that. Mum had told me I mustn't tell anyone.

'You mind your own business,' I said.

Sophie stared at me.

'What did you say?' she said, putting her hands on her hips.

I realised what a fool I'd been. You didn't ever, ever, ever tell Sophie Wallace to mind her own business, especially not on her own territory.

I wished I could rewind and start again. But Sophie was walking towards me now, her eyes narrowed and her chin jutting. I didn't wait to see what she was going to do. I threw my cardboard boxes at her and ran for it. I stupidly didn't run for the lift, I made for the stairs. I ran like crazy, up and up and up, all the way to the tenth floor. I don't know how far Sophie followed me. I wasn't sure if I could hear her footsteps behind me or not, and I was too scared to look round. I didn't even feel safe when I was inside our new flat with the front door slammed shut and I was lying on the bare floorboards in the hall, panting. Sophie was so scary I felt sure she'd be able to push my door in one-handed.

That was two weeks ago. I'd done my level best to keep out of her way ever since. It was easy enough at school because we were in different classes and I didn't hang around the playground. Miss Eagerton had made me her library monitor, which was ace, because I could stay inside and help her tidy the shelves and stamp people's books when they borrowed them.

I just worried about Sophie when I was walking home from school. Like right now. I went in the big entrance to the estate. Someone had spray-painted:

Abandon hope all ye who enter here.

Someone else had written much ruder words too, and there were lots of swirly angry painted pictures. I wished I lived on an estate where people painted lovely things like rainbows and suns and bluebirds. Perhaps Mum might let me paint on my new bedroom walls once we'd given them a new coat of white. They were a dirty grey colour now, with mouldy dark shadows at the top where something had leaked. Dad had said he'd redecorate the whole flat, but he hadn't got started yet. He hadn't tried hard to get a new job either. He just lay on our old sofa and watched television, even if it was a programme he hated.

Mum said Dad wasn't being lazy, he was depressed. But when she came home from looking after all the elderly ladies and found Dad hadn't even washed up the breakfast things or bothered to go out to buy anything for tea, she got angry and she called him lazy then, amongst other things. Then we were all three depressed.

'I hate it here,' I muttered. It was especially horrible not having any friends to play with. It was too far for me to go back to Ladywell Crescent to see all my pals there. And some of them weren't quite as nice to me now I was poor. Even Annabel, my best friend forever, had started going on and on about her new ballet classes, wanting me to go with her. She couldn't seem to understand that we didn't have any money now for me to do fun things like ballet. So she went with Sheena Evans instead, and they kept practising dance steps in the playground. They laughed when I tried to join in too, and said I wasn't doing them properly.

I thought I was just as good at dancing as they were. I tried a little skip and twirl now as I hurried through South block and Centre block, imagining myself in one of those fluffy white ballet dresses, with pink satin slippers.

'Oh my, look at the dancing queen! Dancing baby elephant, more like!' someone shouted raucously from the first-floor balcony.

I looked up, feeling myself going scarlet. Oh no! It was Sophie Wallace herself!

I raced for the stairs – but Sophie charged along the balcony, and as I started going up I heard her jumping down, two steps at a time. I had to get away – I had to get *home*!

I'd have to go in the lift. I always avoided the lift if I could, because it smelt horrible and people said it was always breaking down. But I didn't have any choice. I ran for the lift and jammed my hand on the bell, ringing and ringing – and thank goodness the door opened in a few seconds, just as Sophie came rushing out into the open.

I jumped inside and pressed the button for the top floor, but just as the door was sliding shut Sophie stuck her foot out and stopped it.

'Got you!' she said.

I jabbed madly at the lift buttons, pressing all of them. The door started closing, but Sophie got one shoulder in, and then the other. Then she was there in the lift with me!

'Right!' she said, as the lift shot upwards. 'I'm going to sort you out good and proper, Julie Lyons!'

She took hold of me and shook me hard. Then she lowered her head – and I shut my eyes in terror, waiting for the violent head-butt. What if she broke my nose? Or my front teeth? I gave a little sob.

'Please don't!' I whimpered.

The lift suddenly jolted and made a horrible whining noise. Then it stopped going up. It didn't go down. It stayed still.

We were stuck.

'Oh no!' said Sophie.

I opened my eyes. At least she'd postponed my major head-butt. She was jabbing wildly at the buttons herself.

'It's stuck now, you idiot!' she said, as if it were my fault. She hammered on the door. 'Open!' She started kicking it hard.

'Don't do that!' I said. 'We're between floors! If it opens now we might fall out, down the lift shaft!'

'Well, what do you suggest we do, clever-clogs?'

'We should press the alarm button,' I said.

'Oh yeah? And what good will that do?' said Sophie.

'It will alert the engineers,' I said. 'And they will come and rescue us.'

'*What* engineers?' said Sophie, scornfully. 'You think there's a little bunch of guys in overalls who'll come running to help, just because you've pressed the silly alarm bell? Okay, press it then, and see what happens!'

I pressed it – and nothing at all happened. I pressed again. And again. I hoped that it would make some sort of buzz or ring, but I couldn't hear a thing.

'Oh no, I don't think it's working!' I said.

'That's right. Nothing works on this estate. And no-one ever comes to mend the lifts. The last time this old lady got stuck she was in there for three days, screaming her head off. She was barking mad by the time they got her out – they had to lock her up,' said Sophie.

'That's nonsense,' I said.

'Are you calling me a liar?' said Sophie, stamping right up to me, standing so close our noses were almost touching.

'No! Oh, don't stomp about like that! Didn't you feel the lift rocking?'

'You're scared, aren't you?' said Sophie. 'Go on, admit it, you're scared silly. Look at you, you're shaking!'

'Of course I'm scared!' I said. 'I'm stuck in this horrible smelly lift with the scariest girl on the planet. I'd be barking mad if I wasn't scared!'

Sophie stared at me.

'Do you really think I'm scary then?' she said, as if I'd paid her a supreme compliment.

'I think you're *incredibly* scary.'

'Well, that's right, I am. And once we get out of here I'm going to give you a good going over – but I can't right here and now because you're right, the lift does rock a bit if you move too much – see?' She gave another stamp and the lift shuddered.

'Don't!'

'Shall I do it one more time, eh, just to get you really going?'

'No, please, don't!'

'Sorry, didn't quite hear you,' said Sophie – and she jumped.

It wasn't really a giant jump – but the lift shuddered and just for a moment it seemed as if it was going to plummet downwards. I screamed. Sophie screamed too. We clutched each other, yelling our heads off. Then the lift steadied itself and stayed still. We hung on to each other, gasping. Then we let go quickly. Sophie looked as if she was going to back away.

'Don't move!' I said.

'Don't you tell me what to do!' said Sophie, but she stayed still as a statue.

'It's dangerous!' I said.

'You're such a wimp,' said Sophie – but I knew she was just as scared as me. 'The way you screamed just now!'

'I think we should scream some more,' I said.

'As if that's going to help,' said Sophie, scornfully.

'It might,' I said. 'Someone will hear us – and then they'll get help.'

'Who?' said Sophie. 'No-one will take any notice anyway. People scream all the time on the Bradshaw Estate.'

'Well, sooner or later someone will come looking for us,' I said. 'And if they hear us screaming then they'll know where we are.'

'No-one's going to come looking for *me*,' said Sophie.

'What about your mum?'

'Her?' said Sophie. 'She walked out ages ago. I haven't seen her since

Christmas – and that was a waste of time, she gave me and my brothers rubbish presents.'

'Oh,' I said. I tried to imagine what it would be like to have your mum walk out. It made me feel so sad and lonely I almost felt sorry for Sophie. 'Well, what about your dad?'

'Yeah, what about him?' said Sophie. 'He won't notice I'm not there. He probably won't even suss anything's wrong tomorrow morning. Or the day after. Or the day after *that*.'

'When we'll both be barking mad,' I said. 'Woof woof.'

Sophie stared at me.

'Are you taking the mick? She said, sounding threatening – but then her chin wobbled, and to my astonishment she burst out laughing. 'You're nuts, you are,' she said, but she didn't sound as if she minded too much.

'So I take it *your* mum and dad are going to come running any minute, searching for their precious little darling?' said Sophie.

'Well… probably not,' I said. 'Because my mum's on late shift and won't be home till half past ten. And my dad's home, but I expect he's dozing on the sofa, because that's all he seems to do nowadays, since he lost his job.'

'Oh. Well, that's a fat lot of help. Sooo – we're stuck,' said Sophie.

'Yes. But let's scream anyway,' I said. 'Just in case.'

'Okay. Scream your head off,' said Sophie.

I opened my mouth and screamed a little feebly, while Sophie watched me with her arms folded.

'You scream too. It feels weird screaming all by myself,' I said.

So Sophie threw back her head and screamed too. She screamed so loudly and ferociously I had to put my hands over my ears. Sophie paused, mid scream.

'What are you doing that for?'

'For pity's sake, Sophie, you're deafening me!'

'Well, that's the point, isn't it? We've got to do it loudly.'

'Well, you get first prize for the loudest girl ever.'

'I get first prize for everything in your book. I'm the scariest too, remember?'

'Well – you don't seem *quite* so scary now,' I said, a little sheepishly.

'I'd better duff you up good and proper then. I don't want to damage my reputation,' said Sophie, but she seemed to be joking.

We screamed some more, but Sophie seemed horribly right. No-one came and called to us. I tried shouting 'Dad! Dad! Dad!' but still nothing happened. I imagined my dad on the sofa, staring at the television all afternoon. Maybe all the evening too. Sometimes he seemed to forget all about Mum and me.

'Oh Sophie, what are we going to *do*?' I said.

'I know. I'm starving hungry already, aren't you?'

'Yeah. Oh, hang on!' I fumbled in my school bag. 'I didn't finish my packed lunch!'

There were two squares of tuna and sweetcorn sandwich still left, an apple, and a muesli bar that only had one nibble out of it.

'Brilliant!' said Sophie.

We sat down very gingerly on the dirty lift floor and devoured our feast. The sandwiches were easy to share, but we had no knife for the apple and the muesli bar, so we had to take it in turns to bite. Sophie took an enormous bite of the apple first, and I frowned but didn't say anything, taking a normal size bite myself. Sophie took just a little mouse-bite next, which was fair after all.

'Do you get packed lunches like this every day?' she said.

'Yes. There were more sandwiches and a banana and some raisins in

13

a little box and a carton of orange juice, but I had them at lunchtime.'

'Did you make it up yourself?'

'No, my mum does my packed lunches.'

'You lucky thing.'

I thought about it carefully. 'She always makes too much,' I said. 'I could share with you at school, if you like.'

What was I *saying*, suggesting sharing lunches with Sophie Wallace? We weren't best friends, we were deadly enemies. And yet now, squashed up together in the lift, we seemed to be getting along just fine.

'You won't want to go round with me at school,' said Sophie, twiddling a strand of her hair. 'You're one of the posh nobs.'

'No I'm not. Well, not any more. And I quite like the idea of going round with you, so long as you don't beat me up.'

'Can't I beat you up a little bit, just for fun?' said Sophie – but I knew she was joking now.

'What on earth are we going to do, stuck in the lift for hours and hours?' I said. I jiggled the books in my school bag. 'I know, we could do all our homework. And fill in all the work sheets and the tests at the back.'

Sophie stared at me, wrinkling her nose. She said a very rude word in response – and I burst out laughing.

'Only joking!' I said. I found a blank page in my notebook. 'Let's play hangman instead.'

It was great fun playing hangman with Sophie. She thought up the most extraordinary words and drew the little hung pinman very graphically, with his tongue hanging out. We got so involved in our game that we almost forgot we were stuck in the lift. We both jumped when we heard someone calling.

'Julie! *Julie!* Julie, where are you?'

'It's my dad!' I said. 'Oh, he came looking for me after all! Dad, Dad, I'm in here, stuck in the lift!'

I waited, but he didn't seem to hear.

'You shout for me, Sophie. You're much louder than me,' I said.

'*JULIE AND I ARE STUCK IN THE LIFT!*' Sophie yelled.

We heard my dad banging on the lift door.

'Press the alarm bell, Julie!' he shouted.

'We did that, ages ago,' Sophie shouted back. 'And nothing's happened.'

'Well, don't worry, I'll get help,' Dad shouted.

And he did! He called the *Fire Service* – and they came in a great big fire engine and cranked the lift down and pulled the door open and rescued us! Half the kids on the estate had all gathered round excitedly – and there was a big cheer when we came out. There was even a local reporter, who wrote about us in the newspaper!

Two young friends were stuck in a lift on the Bradshaw Estate for many hours! he wrote.

It wasn't really many hours. It wasn't even one hour – so Sophie and I didn't go barking mad. But the *two young friends* bit was true, because we really are best friends now. Sophie doesn't seem one bit scary now that I know her.

She comes to tea a lot, and sometimes she has a sleepover at my place. Mum's a bit worried that she might be a bad influence, but Dad likes her a lot. And guess what, Dad's going to try to train for a brand new job. He wants to be a fireman!

The End

My Christmas Tree

When I was a little girl we had a very tiny artificial tree with a few glass baubles and a chocolate parrot wrapped in shiny red and green foil. I longed to eat the parrot, but my mum would have had a fit if I'd so much as licked it!

Nowadays I choose a real tree each year because I think it looks much nicer — though you do get heaps of pine needles on the carpet! I have fairy lights and lots and lots of decorations. I don't go for tasteful colour themes — I have every colour, and all different types of decorations.

My favourite is a little handmade angel with glass wings. She was specially made for me by a friend and she flies at the top of my tree every year. She shares her perch with a fairy doll with a fluffy white skirt and pointy toes.

I'm also very fond of this shiny Father Christmas with a giant stick of peppermint candy given to me by my American friend, Nancy.

16

I have a glass reindeer who gallops among the lower branches, and some weird little quirky ornaments like this tiny black handbag with a red tassel.

I like to have lots of birds perched here and there on my tree. I have heaps of glass birds and also some feathery ones. Look at this magnificent gothic black peacock.

There are many coloured glass balls and tin hearts and tiny people — and of course I have a special little stripy wool cat to please Jacob.

Did You Know?

Blaine from the JW Mag team has a glass reindeer on her tree that's identical to Jacky's!

Write about your own favourite tree decoration here —

My favourite tree decoration is a golden bow. I've had it for ages and it always goes on the best place on the tree.

17

Ask Jacky

Everything you wanted to know about your favourite author!

Reply | Reply All | Forward | Junk | ✕

To: My favourite author!

From: Alice, Clackmannanshire

Did you ever think about giving up on your dream of becoming a published writer?

I always wanted to be a writer from when I was six years old, but I wasn't sure I'd ever get published!

Jacqueline Wilson — SAPPHIRE BATTERSEA — ILLUSTRATED BY NICK SHARRATT

Reply | Reply All | Forward | Junk | ✕

To: Jacqueline

From: Hannah, Southport

If you could go back to any time in the past, what era would you go to?

That's an easy one, Hannah — I'd go back to Victorian times, and then I could find out exactly what it was like, so that I'd be able to fill my Hetty Feather books with all sorts of fascinating details!

Reply | Reply All | Forward | Junk | ✕

To: Dame Jacqueline Wilson

From: Emily, Belfast

Would you ever trade the job and life you have for another one?

I think I like my own life, though I wouldn't mind being a bit younger and fitter!

Reply | Reply All | Forward | Junk | ✕

To: Jacqueline

From: Lucy, Manchester

Do you have a special pen you use to write all your stories with? I use a special pheasant feather I found lying in the middle of the road!

I don't have a special pen — I use any old black felt pen — but I do use lovely Italian marbled notebooks. I hope you enjoy writing stories with your pheasant feather!

18

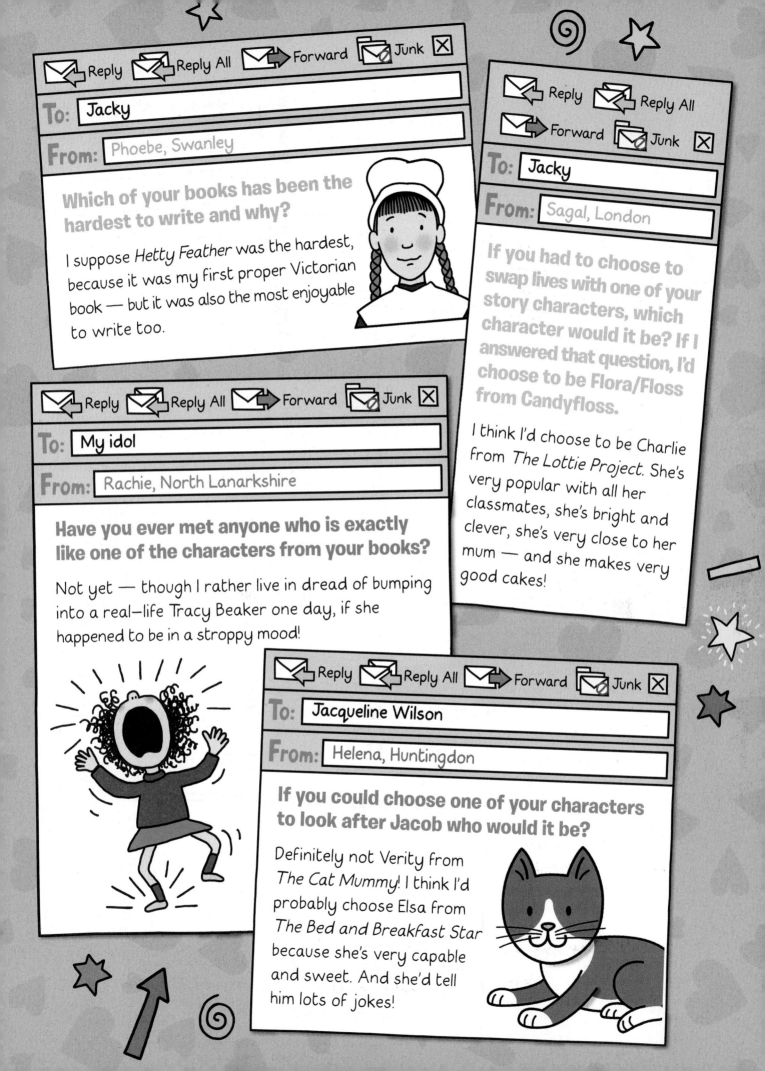

Reply **Reply All** **Forward** **Junk** ☒

To: Jacky

From: Phoebe, Swanley

Which of your books has been the hardest to write and why?

I suppose *Hetty Feather* was the hardest, because it was my first proper Victorian book — but it was also the most enjoyable to write too.

Reply **Reply All** **Forward** **Junk** ☒

To: Jacky

From: Sagal, London

If you had to choose to swap lives with one of your story characters, which character would it be? If I answered that question, I'd choose to be Flora/Floss from Candyfloss.

I think I'd choose to be Charlie from *The Lottie Project*. She's very popular with all her classmates, she's bright and clever, she's very close to her mum — and she makes very good cakes!

Reply **Reply All** **Forward** **Junk** ☒

To: My idol

From: Rachie, North Lanarkshire

Have you ever met anyone who is exactly like one of the characters from your books?

Not yet — though I rather live in dread of bumping into a real–life Tracy Beaker one day, if she happened to be in a stroppy mood!

Reply **Reply All** **Forward** **Junk** ☒

To: Jacqueline Wilson

From: Helena, Huntingdon

If you could choose one of your characters to look after Jacob who would it be?

Definitely not Verity from *The Cat Mummy*! I think I'd probably choose Elsa from *The Bed and Breakfast Star* because she's very capable and sweet. And she'd tell him lots of jokes!

Winter

Cosy up with a mug of hot choccy and do all this...

⭐ Fabulous fashion designing
⭐ Write perfect poems
⭐ Play the poem game
⭐ Take the chilly puzzle challenge
⭐ Draw Em's reindeer, Dancer
⭐ Make a bird seed cake

e It!

Draw lots of pretty bracelets and bangles on Melissa's arm.

Transform this boring bag into a purse fit for a princess!

Pink and girly, glam and glitzy — that's my fashion style!

Melissa

Inspirational Ideas

- ☑ Flowers
- ☑ Pink
- ☑ Kittens
- ☑ Sequins
- ☑ Hearts

23

Go fashion crazy and let your imagination run wild!

DON'T TOUCH WHAY YOU CAN'T AFFORD

Make brill badges! Add slogans and funny cartoon drawings.

Ruby

Inspirational Ideas
☑ Gothic
☑ Ponytail
☑ Curls
☑ Blonde
☑ BOOM

Long, wavy tresses or funky punk? Have fun creating a brand new hairstyle for Ruby!

Design gorgeous hair clips for Garnet's friends to admire.

I want to look too cool for school!

Garnet

Decorate Garnet's dull school satchel with cute badges, pins and accessories.

Inspirational Ideas

- ☑ Charms
- ☑ Keyring
- ☑ Corsage
- ☑ Cherries
- ☑ Gems

How to Write A Poem

What is a poem?

A poem is another way to say something or tell a story. You can pick anything you like to write about such as a favourite person or event, time of the year, pet, hobby or thing.

Start by writing some notes on your subject. How will you turn these into a poem? There are lots of different methods, so here are some ideas —

Acrostic Poems

An acrostic poem starts with any name or word and the subject of the poem is based on that word. Writing an acrostic poem is easy and fun, here's how —

Write your starting word so it reads **down** the page. Now think about what you'd like to say or describe about the word. For example:

Jumping around
And playing in the grass
Cutest little cat
Observing the birds
Bundles of fun!

A Rhyming Poem

The same lines in each verse should be the rhyming lines. It helps to tap out a rhythm so each verse sounds the same. Look at these examples —

He met a girl with eyes of blue
And she was good at cooking too
He knew his love for her was true
A butcher boy called Bertie

To prove to her that he did care
He took her out to see the fair
Some cotton candy they did share
Sapphire and her Bertie

The first three lines rhyme and, although the last lines don't, they end with the same word. You can say the same things with a different rhyming pattern —

Bertie met a fiery girl
With eyes of sparkling blue
And once he'd tried her apple pies
He knew his love was true

He called upon her house one day
They walked out to the fair
He held her hand to show his love
And bought treats for them to share

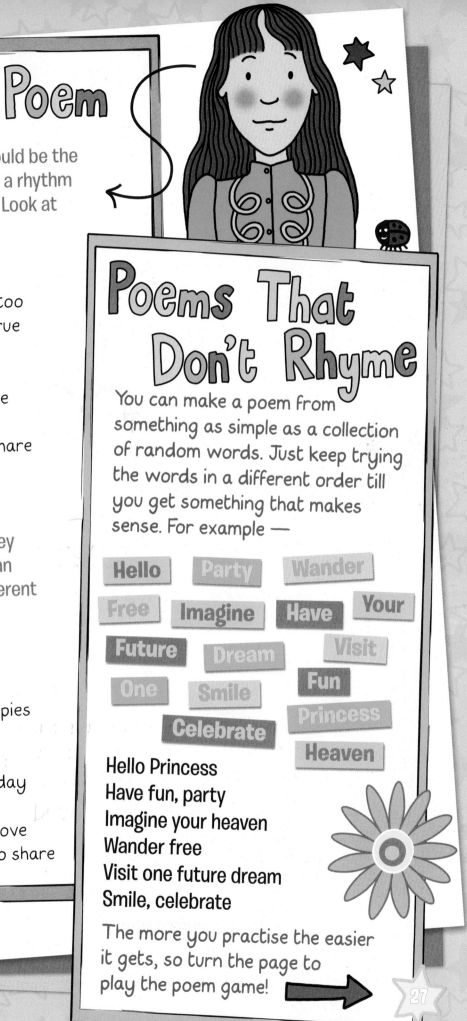

Poems That Don't Rhyme

You can make a poem from something as simple as a collection of random words. Just keep trying the words in a different order till you get something that makes sense. For example —

Hello   Party   Wander
Free   Imagine   Have   Your
Future   Dream   Visit
One   Smile   Fun
Celebrate   Princess
Heaven

Hello Princess
Have fun, party
Imagine your heaven
Wander free
Visit one future dream
Smile, celebrate

The more you practise the easier it gets, so turn the page to play the poem game! ➡

You'll Need
* An old newspaper
* Buttons or badges for counters
* A dice

How to play:
* Cut out lots of words from the newspaper headlines and put them in a bowl.
* Roll the dice and follow the instructions on each square you land on.
* If you land on a sapphire gemstone take two words from the bowl and put them aside
* When you've finished the game arrange the words you've collected into a poem.

35.

36.

37.

38.

39.

40. You shout at Mr Buchanan. Go back 2 spaces.

41.

42.

43.

44.

45.

You get letters from Mama and Jem. Move on 1 space.

34.

33.

32.

31.

30.

46. Sarah gives you extra apple pie. Go forward 1 space.

47.

48.

49.

29. Mrs B sends you to bed without supper. Miss a turn.

25.

26.

27.

28.

50. Your candle burns out before you finish reading. Go back 1 space.

Finish

Cool Quizzes

Puzzles with a frosty feeling!

✫ Chilly Creatures ✫

Can you find these snow-loving animals in the grid?

Huskies   Penguin

Seal   Polar Bear

Puffin   Reindeer

Snow Leopard

Wolf   Arctic Fox

Narwhal Whale

Moose   Caribou

```
R D E M M M Z N L U J B R
E R S M W Z A I F G A Y J
I A O M O E A I F E R O D
N P O Q S U T I Z F U U M
D O M U O B I A B F C P P
E E P Q H B J A R F P A N
E L A H W J L R Y C C U H
R W T E O L A H W R S P H
E O N P P S A I K S A M H
C N A R C U T B C F B U X T
J S Y E E N G I C U O I N
W O L F D S Y E O M Y P
```

★ Snowball Scramble! ★

Which JW characters are hidden in the snowballs?

1. _____

2. _____

3. _____

4. _____

30

Double Disaster!

Whoops! Can you find six differences between these two pictures?

Cool Crossword

How quickly can you solve it?

ACROSS

5. A mug of hot _____ will warm you up! (9)

7. You wear these on your hands to keep them cosy (6)

8. Whee! You can ride this down a snowy hill (6)

9. A fun winter sport — all you need are shoes with blades (7)

10. These trees are used for Christmas trees (3)

DOWN

1. In *Starring Tracy Beaker*, Cam and Tracy have egg and _____ for their Christmas dinner (5)

2. An icy sculpture made by frozen running water (6)

3. We sing these at Christmas time (6)

4. These animals pull Santa's sleigh (8)

6. This snowy gentleman has a carrot for his nose! (7)

31

How To Draw Dancer!

1. Begin by drawing the shape of Dancer's head. Give her two small floppy ears and a cute round nose.

2. Draw a curve for Dancer's jaw and the outline of her two front legs. Sketch a wavy line for the frilly hem of her dress.

3. Add a pair of antlers and detail to her ears. Draw her bodice and lots more frills. Give Dancer a pair of hooves and sketch her back legs.

4. Draw her eyes and sketch sweet little ballet shoes on Dancer's feet. Finally, use lots of pale pink and brown to colour her in!

Which JW book did Dancer the reindeer puppet appear in?

Have fun designing festive outfits for Dancer! How about a Santa-style dress?

Make a Bird Seed Cake

A winter treat for feathered friends!

You'll need:
- ☆ Plastic cup or empty yoghurt pot
- ☆ 200g of lard
- ☆ Bird seed mix
- ☆ Raffia or string
- ☆ Twig

Other treats to add:

Peanuts | Mealworms

Chopped apple | Bacon rind

1. Cut a piece of string or raffia and fold in half. Tie a knot about 5cm from the top.

2. Place the cup on top of a sponge or folded tea towel. Make a hole by pushing a pencil down through the centre of the bottom and into the sponge.

3. Thread the string through the hole so the loop and knot are on the outside.

4. Tie the twig across the bottom of the cup with the other end of the string.

5. Put the lard into a mixing bowl. Ask an adult to help you melt it in the microwave for 20 seconds at a time until it's soft and creamy.

6. Mix in the bird seed and any other treats you want to add.

7. Tightly push the mix into the cup with a teaspoon and leave to set in the fridge.

8. Finish by asking an adult to carefully cut off the cup. Now hang the seed cake outside for the birds to enjoy.

34

Spring

You'll love this springy stuff...

Jacky's Spring Things!

More JW secrets revealed!

I love Spring! I like going for a walk in Richmond Park when the azaleas come out in the Isabella Plantation. The hedges are brilliant pink, peach, scarlet, crimson and magenta, stretching as far as you can see. This is the 'magic garden' that the children visit in *Lily Alone*.

I like it when all the baby animals and birds are born. The little fawns in the park are especially gorgeous.

I like starting a brand new book, writing that first chapter in a beautiful notebook.

I like wearing a new summer dress or t-shirt.

I like it when it stays lighter in the evenings and I can go for walks along the river after tea.

I like the first time I get to sit out in the sunshine in the garden and can stretch out and read. Jacob loves to sunbathe too!

I like it when the hellebores and primroses are all over the garden — and then the cherry tree comes into flower.

Are You Just Like Jacky?

Write a list of your favourite spring things and see if you match with JW!

I like all the Spring literary festivals! This year I've been to Dubai, which was fabulous and exotic. I also like going to the Hay—on—Wye book festival and spending time in all the second—hand bookshops.

Spring Sketch & Doodle

DRAW AND DESIGN, JUST LIKE NICK!

Baby Bunny

1. Draw two long ears on top of an oval head. Add a curved line for the bunny's back.

2. Fill in your bunny's back leg and front paws.

3. Draw eyes, a nose, whiskers and a fluffy tail before colouring in your sketch.

Cheery Daffodil

1. Start by sketching the trumpet shape in the centre of the daffodil. Draw petals all the way round.

2. Draw a long stem and one leaf.

3. Add a couple more leaves to your daffodil. Use your brightest yellow and green pens to colour it in.

Cute Chick

1. Begin by drawing the shape of the chick's body and head.

2. Draw a curved line for its wing and two short legs. Draw two little triangles for a beak.

3. Give your chick eyes and feet before adding colour to your sketch.

Little Lamb

1. Draw two round ears and the outline of your lamb's back. Don't forget to add a short floppy tail!

2. Fill in the lamb's four legs and draw an oval for its face.

3. Colour the hooves black and finish the face with a nose, mouth and eyes.

Draw with me!

Flower Wreath

So sweet and so simple!

You will need:
- Patterned paper
- Buttons
- Glue

Trace these templates then cut out different sized
flower shapes in different patterned papers.

Photography and project courtesy of **hobby**craft

Arrange the
flowers in a ring
shape then begin
sticking together,
overlapping the
petals.

Glue a button to
the middle of
each of the
flowers to finish.

**Make It
For Mum!**
This pretty wreath
makes a great gift for
Mother's Day.

Picnic In The Park

Lily has a special treat packed inside her picnic basket. Solve the puzzles to reveal all...

HIDE AND SEEK

I'm searching the park for Pixie and the twins! Fit these parkland animals into the grid and their hiding place will be revealed.

Kingfisher Mouse
Deer Squirrel
Rabbit Hedgehog

B
I
D
E

Put the 2nd letter of this answer in the 2nd picnic box. Put the 6th letter of this answer in the 8th picnic box

ICE CREAM TREAT

Bliss wants an ice cream. Solve the riddles below to discover her favourite flavour.

My 1st is in van but not in man.
My 2nd is in cane but not in cone.
My 3rd is in crown but not in crowd.
My 4th is in chip but not in chop.
My 5th is in spell but not in spend.
My 6th is in fold but not in fond.
My 7th is in pan but not in pin.

_ _ _ _ _ _ _

Put the 2nd letter of this answer in the 5th picnic box.

SUMMER SPORTS

Uh–oh! Baxter has disturbed a group of people playing K_ _ _ _ _ _ in the park!

Cross out the letters that appear three times to find out what game they were playing.

M C A R X
I B M C L
A W K M A
W E B L W
L X T X B

Put the 1st letter of this answer in the 4th picnic box.
Put the 4th letter of this answer in the 1st picnic box.
Put the 5th letter of this answer in the 6th picnic box.

PECKISH POOCH!

Oops! A naughty dog has run off with some of the picnic food!
Fill in the missing letter on each line to make two new words. The name of the dog will appear in the shaded boxes.

D	R	I		A	R	C	E	L
F	R	E		S	S	A	Y	
S	T	U	M		R	A	W	N
C	L	A		I	C	K	L	E
T	R	E		L	E	P	H	A	N	T
B	O	A		U	B	B	E	R

Put the 1st letter of this answer in the 3rd picnic box. Put the 5th letter of this answer in the 7th picnic box.

1 2 3 4 5 6 7 8

Fabulous Finales!

Write your own endings for your favourite characters!

Lola Rose

What happens next?

The final chapter:

Just when things seem like they couldn't get any worse, Lola Rose's violent dad makes an appearance and threatens to ruin everything. Fortunately, brave Auntie Barbara is on hand to see him off and take care of Lola Rose, Kendall and Mum. She offers them the chance of a new life and a new home...

- ⭐ Will Dad stay out of their lives forever?
- ⭐ Will Lola Rose and Kendall ever go back to using their real names?
- ⭐ Can Auntie Barbara give them the safe home they dream of?

Little Darlings

What happens next?

The final chapter:

Destiny has been reunited with her famous dad, Danny Kilman. She's all set to star in a special TV show, thanks to Sunset, her sister. Danny's wife, Suzy, is not at all happy — will she let Destiny into her home and her heart?

- ⭐ Will Destiny shoot to stardom?
- ⭐ How will Sweetie and Ace react to having a new sister?
- ⭐ Will Danny be a good father to Destiny?

felt tips

Bad Girls

What happens next?

The final chapter:

Mandy feels terribly lonely without Tanya, but things start to look up when she makes friends with Arthur and nasty Kim finally stops bullying her. When a postcard from Tanya drops through her letterbox, Mandy can't help but hope that they'll meet again one day...

_____
_____
_____
_____

★ Will Mandy and Tanya ever be reunited?
★ Do you think Kim will go back to her bullying ways?
★ Will Mandy and Arthur stay friends forever?

The Suitcase Kid

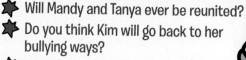 **What happens next?**

The final chapter:

Andy is over the moon with her new baby sister, Zoë. Actually, she's feeling a lot happier about everything — Graham is a great mate, Crystal is sweet, Zen's okay, and Katie... well, there's still a long way to go before the girls will ever be friends!

_____
_____
_____
_____

☆ Will Andy ever go back to Mulberry Cottage?
☆ How do you think the new baby will change things?
☆ Will Katie and Andy become friends?

Tracy's Horrible

Create a silly story full of drama and doom!

What to do:

Roll a dice and pick a choice that matches with your number from section A. Repeat to make choices from every section. When you've made all the choices, read them out to reveal your silly story.

(A) My plans for today were...

1. playing dares with
2. watching a film with
3. baking cakes with
4. peeling potatoes with
5. building a secret den with
6. being annoying with

(B)

1. my mum, fabulous Hollywood movie star!
2. a large dog and a teeny tiny kitten.
3. Pathetic Peter.
4. Football and Alexander.
5. Jacqueline Wilson.
6. Nick Sharratt.

Make up your own choices for even more fun!

(C) But then I heard that...

1. The Dumping Ground was covered with giant killer bees!
2. my school had fallen into an enormous, lava–filled hole!
3. poisonous people–eating flowers were springing up everywhere!
4. books were flying up the high street and snapping at people!
5. it was raining slimy slugs and creepy cockroaches!
6. everyone had turned into evil Tracy Beaker impostors!

Happenings!

Play on your own or with your besties!

D So to get to the site of the trouble I...
1. skated on pink glittery roller skates.
2. bounced on a huge purple space hopper.
3. walked on my hands all the way there.
4. put on a snorkel and pretended I was swimming.
5. danced and twirled like a girly ballerina.
6. did cartwheels and forward rolls.

The Dumping Ground

E When I got there I discovered...
1. a malevolent magician!
2. a wicked witch!
3. an obnoxious goblin!
4. a dreadful doctor!
5. a villainous Count!
6. Justine Littlewood, No. 1 enemy!

Justine

F So I saved the day by...
1. slathering them in freezing strawberry milkshake!
2. tying them up with old tights!
3. pelting them with jammy doughnuts!
4. squirting them with bug spray!
5. trapping them under itchy blankets!
6. swatting them with an enormous tennis racquet!

milkshake

Play again and again for different story outcomes.

Forever Friends!

Reunite Gemma with her bestie, Alice.

START

Summer

ice lolly

yum!

Sunshine funshine things to do...

- ⭐ Read Jacky and Nick's holiday secrets
- ⭐ Start a summer book club — our kit has all you need!
- ⭐ Find your perfect summer activity
- ⭐ Make a beautiful beach bag

Jacky and Nick's
Holiday Scrapbook!

SECRETS REVEALED!

Every year Nick and I try to go on a little holiday together.

Last year we stayed in a Gothic Temple in Stowe. It was an amazing place, like a little fairytale palace, heavily decorated inside as well as out. It even had a belvedere (little tower) and the first night we stood at the top at midnight and watched fireworks!

The Temple was in the midst of landscape gardens where there were many other statues and grottos — and even some sheep! Stowe landscape garden is owned by The National Trust, so during the day there were visitors wandering in the grounds — but in the evenings we had the whole place to ourselves.

Can you name a JW character who watches fireworks from a tower window?

Photography by Trish Beswick

I also went to North Norfolk. I think Holkham beach is my favourite beach in the whole of England — and it's so huge it never gets crowded. It's my dream to have a little cottage nearby.

I go to Paris with my daughter Emma every year. We go shopping and visit an art gallery every morning, sit in the Tuileries Gardens and read in the afternoon, and explore every evening. Emma speaks fluent French which is an enormous help!

My Best Trip...

Nick loves to go skiing, but Jacky prefers a hot sunny beach. If you could go on your dream holiday, what would it be? Write about it here

My Dream Holiday!

....

....

....

....

....

ANSWER:
Jodie from My Sister Jodie

Summer Book Club Kit!

Everything you need to start your own club!

Invite your friends!

Find Book Buddies!

Every good Book Club needs members who ♥ books! Think about who might want to join **your** book club. Aim to invite 4–8 people. You could ask your BF, classmates or family members. Ask them if they...

⭐ **Love to read?**
☆ **Like chatting with friends?**
☆ **Enjoy group activities?**

If they answer '**yes**', invite them along!

Write the names of your Book Club members here.

Club Leader (me!)

....

Book Club Members

....

....

....

....

....

....

....

Name Game!

Play along to pick the perfect name for your Book Club.

Choose a colour

Dickens   Blyton

Wilson   Shakespeare

Dahl   Rowling

Roll a dice

1. Book
2. Word
3. Story
4. Tale
5. Writer
6. Bookworm

Now pick a picture

Club

Pals

Friends

Buddies

Stars

Gang

I picked pink, rolled a 3 and chose the picture of Tanya and Mandy. So my Book Club is called Wilson's Story Friends.

Our Book Club name is _____'s

_____ _____

ice lolly

yum!

Book Club Kit!

You don't need any special equipment to start a Book Club. Everyone can bring along:

⭐ **A notebook**
⭐ **Pen**
⭐ **Book Club badge**

(find them on page 59!)

dream house

Meeting Place

You can take it in turns to hold your Book Club meetings at your homes, or you could meet up...

In the library

In the school playground at lunchtime

At your favourite café

At the park — just take along some rugs to sit on.

In the garden if it's a nice sunny day!

At your local youth club

icecream

yum!

Brain Boosting Snacks!

Make these tasty snacks for your next Book Club meeting.

Gemma's Fruity Smoothies

Fruity and refreshing to quench your thirst!

Makes four drinks!

You will need:
- ★ 1 cup of fresh orange juice
- ★ 2 cups of strawberries
- ★ 2 strawberry yoghurts
- ★ Ice cubes

1. Ask an adult to blend all of the ingredients in a blender until the liquid becomes thick and smooth.

2. Pour into glasses and top with a straw!

yum!

Biscuits' Brekkie Bars

Treat your Book Club friends to these yummy cereal bars.

Easy to bake, delicious to eat!

You will need:
- ☆ 225g oats
- ☆ 25g crushed cornflakes
- ☆ 75g sugar
- ☆ 75g golden syrup
- ☆ 110g butter
- ☆ 1 banana, mashed

1. Preheat the oven to 170°C. Mix the sugar, syrup and butter in a pan and melt over a low heat. Ask an adult to help.

2. Stir in the crushed cornflakes and oats to the mixture before adding the mashed banana.

3. Grease a baking tray with butter and pour in the mixture. Pop in the oven for 25–30 minutes or until golden.

4. Leave to cool before enjoying.

Top Tip! Add your favourite dried fruits to the mixture —cranberries, sultanas, cherries and apricots all taste lovely!

ice lolly
yum!

Pick A Book!

Choose a book and get reading!

Now that you have your Book Club members gathered, it's time to choose the first book for the group to read.

You can:
- Take it in turns to pick a book
- Vote for someone's suggestion
- Pick titles out of a hat

Our first Book Club choice is:

Title ....

Author ....

Some of you may already own the book you have chosen to read but others can borrow it from the library or a friend, or buy their own copy if they have the money.

Top Tip!

Everyone reads at a different pace, so agree a timescale, such as two weeks, before meeting up again to talk about the book. Already read it? Give it another go to refresh your memory and see if you missed anything the first time round!

Book Review

Scan or copy this page and give a few to each member, or get everyone to copy it into their notebook so they can review the book.

My Book Review!

By ....

I have just read ....

This book was written by ....

....

The story was about ....

....

I didn't like ....

My favourite part was ....

....

I would change ....

Overall, I would rate this book:

☐ Excellent
☐ Good
☐ Okay
☐ Disappointing
☐ Boring

Fill in your Book Review before each meeting.

Chit-Chat!

Now that you've all read the book it's time to share your views and opinions. Use the Chat Cards to get talking about the story — pick a card from a deck and match the suit to find a topic to talk about.

♠ Plot

Talk about...

- **Twists and turns**
- **Unexpected events**
- Favourite part
- What you would change

♥ Characters

Talk about...

- Who you liked best
- Who you liked least
- **What happens to the characters**
- The main character

♣ Ending

Talk about...

- Cliffhanger?
- Happily-ever-after?
- Disappointing?
- **Desperate to read the sequel?**

♦ Author

Talk about...

- **Writing style — fun, witty, serious or sad?**
- **Description and setting the scene**
- Other books by same author
- Compare with your fave author

58

Find Your Summer Fun Activity!

What will YOU get up to this summer?

START — I like to keep busy.

— NO → I love to explore!

— YES → My friends come round all the time.

My nose is always in a book!

— YES → I'm a whizz in the kitchen.

— NO → I'm super-organised.

I love to explore! — YES → I love a good mystery!

I'm super-organised. — YES → I love a good mystery!

I'm super-organised. — NO → Lazing in the sunshine is fab!

I'm a whizz in the kitchen. — NO → I'm super-organised.

I'm a whizz in the kitchen. — YES → Lazing in the sunshine is fab!

My nose is always in a book! — NO → I'm super-organised.

My friends come round all the time. — NO → I love to explore!

My friends come round all the time. — YES → Hidden Hideaway

I love a good mystery! — YES → Terrific Treasure Hunt

I love a good mystery! — NO → Hidden Hideaway

Lazing in the sunshine is fab! — NO → I love a good mystery!

Lazing in the sunshine is fab! — YES → Lazy Ice Lollies

Hidden Hideaway

Build a cool den with your friends! Ask an adult if you can put up a tent in the back garden or simply transform the shed — just add some homely touches with scatter cushions, tasty treats and your favourite things.

Terrific Treasure Hunt

Have fun organising your very own Treasure Hunt! You can hide the clues all round your garden — put on your thinking cap and write clever riddles and rhymes to lead your friends to a fantastic prize!

Lazy Ice Lollies

Fill a lolly mould with your favourite fruits, add some juice and pop in the freezer. Now that you're armed with a fruity lolly, JW book, sunglasses and sun cream you can kick back and relax in the sunshine — bliss!

61

Make a Beautiful Beach Bag

Turn an old vest top into a summer bag in three easy steps!

1. Turn the vest inside out. Use a double thickness of strong thread to make a line of small running stitches across the bottom, just above the hem.

2. Pull the stitches tight then pass the needle through the edge of the fabric a few times to make a secure knot.

3. Turn the right way out. You now have a bag perfect for the beach! Why not decorate it with some pretty ribbons and badges?

Jacqueline Wilson

Autumn

Say bye, bye to boredom with...

- ⭐ Friendship fortune game
- ⭐ Awesome autumn activity file
- ⭐ Nick helps you draw Marigold
- ⭐ Reveal Jodie's tower treasure
- ⭐ Make horrible Halloween snacks
- ⭐ Find the perfect story ending

Find Your Friendship Fortune

Friendship secrets revealed!

How to play:

⭐ Add together the number of letters in your name.

⭐ Add together the number of letters in your friend's name.

⭐ Now add the two totals together to find your friendship number.

For example:

Jacqueline Wilson = 16 letters.
Nick Sharratt = 12 letters.
16 + 12 = 28
2 + 8 = 10
1 + 0 = 1
So Jacky and Nick's friendship number is 1.

1. You are India and Treasure

⭐ You'll always be there for each other.

BF Fun: Have fun solving the puzzles in this annual.

Secret Code Word: Journal.

2. You are Floss and Susan

⭐ Best friends forever.

BF Fun: Organise a fun sleepover for just the two of you.

Secret Code Word: Chips.

3. You are Destiny and Sunset

⭐ Ultimate talented duo!

BF Fun: Dress up in glam clothes and perform a pop concert!

Secret Code Word: Star.

4. You are Mandy and Tanya

⭐ Perfect pals.

BF Fun: Create a collage of all your favourite JW characters.

Secret Code Word: Rainbow.

5. **You are Vicky and Jade**
⭐ Friends for life.

BF Fun: Dress up in your cringiest clothes and put on a fashion show.

Secret Code Word: Ghost.

6. **You are Gemma and Alice**
⭐ Nothing will ever come between you.

BF Fun: Bake sweet treats together. Yum!

Secret Code Word: Cake.

7. **You are Daisy and Emily**
⭐ Sleepover buddies.

BF Fun: Give each other a funny hairstyle.

Secret Code Word: Pizza.

8. **You are Ruby and Garnet**
⭐ Fun-loving duo!

BF Fun: Write and star together in your very own play!

Secret Code Word: Opal.

9. **You are Tracy and Peter**
⭐ Mischievous mates!

BF Fun: Have a giggle at the cringes in JW Mag.

Secret Code Word: Socks!

Shhh... Shhh...

TOP SECRET!

Here's a few fun ways to use your super secret code word...

Sign your messages to your BF with your code word instead of your name to keep your messages totally private!

Write your code word on a small piece of paper and roll it up. Tie with a piece of ribbon and attach it to a necklace or bracelet. Make two — one for you, one for your BF.

Share your code word with your closest friends and use it as a secret password for your next Book Club meeting. Only those who know the code can enter!

End every text to your BF with your secret code word. Over and out!

Shhh... Shhh...

Nature Treasure Hunt

Take a woodland or park walk and see how many of these autumn treasures you can find. Tick them off as you go and give yourself points for each thing you spot. Play with your BF to see who scores the most.

☐ Big autumn leaf	1 point	
☐ Blackberries	3 points	
☐ Pine cones	3 points	
☐ Acorns	4 points	
☐ Conkers or chestnuts	4 points	
☐ Fallen twigs	1 point	
☐ Helicopter seeds	2 points	
☐ Rosehips	3 points	
☐ Moss	2 points	
☐ Squirrel	5 points	
☐ Feather	2 points	
☐ Robin	5 points	

YOU

YOUR BF

Total: ____/33

Total: ____/33

Did You Know?

The Japanese absolutely love looking for trees with the most beautiful autumn leaves. The pastime is called **Momijigari** which means **red leaves** hunting.

Take a photo of some fiery coloured trees and stick it here.

SCRAP & SKETCH BOOK

Colour and design with gorgeous autumn shades.

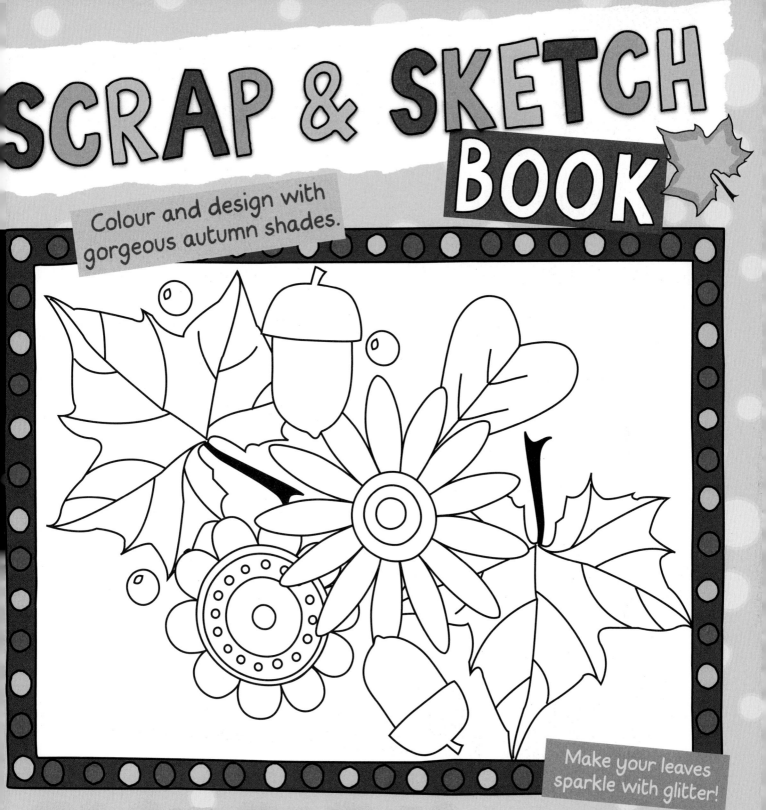

Make your leaves sparkle with glitter!

Make Paints From Plants!

You can make natural paints with blackberries and plants such as moss, grass or dandelion flowers and leaves — don't pick anything poisonous!

● Grind the plants or berries with a mortar and pestle.

● Make each colour separately.

● Add a little water to make pastes thin enough to paint with.

● Take care not to stain your clothes.

More ideas on the next page

SCRAPBOOK

RECYCLING!

1 Give newspaper a vintage look by rubbing over it with a wet used teabag. Leave the paper to dry.

2 Cut out some shapes from card using the template patterns below.

3 Decorate the shapes with the aged newspaper and paper scraps. Stick the paper to the front with glue or tape then trim like this.

Clip the decorated pegs on to a line of string to hold your precious sketches and photos!

Trace these autumn shapes and cut patterns from paper to draw round.

SHAPES

You'll Need

- ★ String, garden twine or raffia
- ☆ Wooden pegs
- ☆ Card — old boxes and cereal packets are perfect
- ★ Old newspaper
- ☆ Wrapping paper scraps
- ☆ Used teabags
- ★ Twigs
- ☆ Glue or double-sided sticky tape

4 Tear the edges of the paper and add different layers for a scrapbook style.

5 Add some twig and string decorations too.

6 Now stick a peg to the back of each finished shape.

How To Draw Marigold!

1. Start by sketching a wavy line for the outline of Marigold's hair. Draw a 'V' shape for her face, and add two small ears with little hoop earrings.

2. Draw two shorter wavy lines for Marigold's fringe. Sketch her neck and shoulders before drawing her arm and the outline of her top.

3. Sketch lots more wavy lines to create a wild mane of hair. Fill in Marigold's eyes, nose and mouth, and complete the outline of her vest top.

4. Very carefully, add tattoos to Marigold's arms and chest. Now use your pens or pencils to colour her in!

Try your hand at designing your very own intricate tattoos on Marigold's body.

Treasure In The Tower

What has Jodie found in the tower room? Solve all the puzzles to find out!

Party Time!

Melchester College is having a party! Fit everyone correctly into the grid below and a special surprise will appear in the shaded boxes.

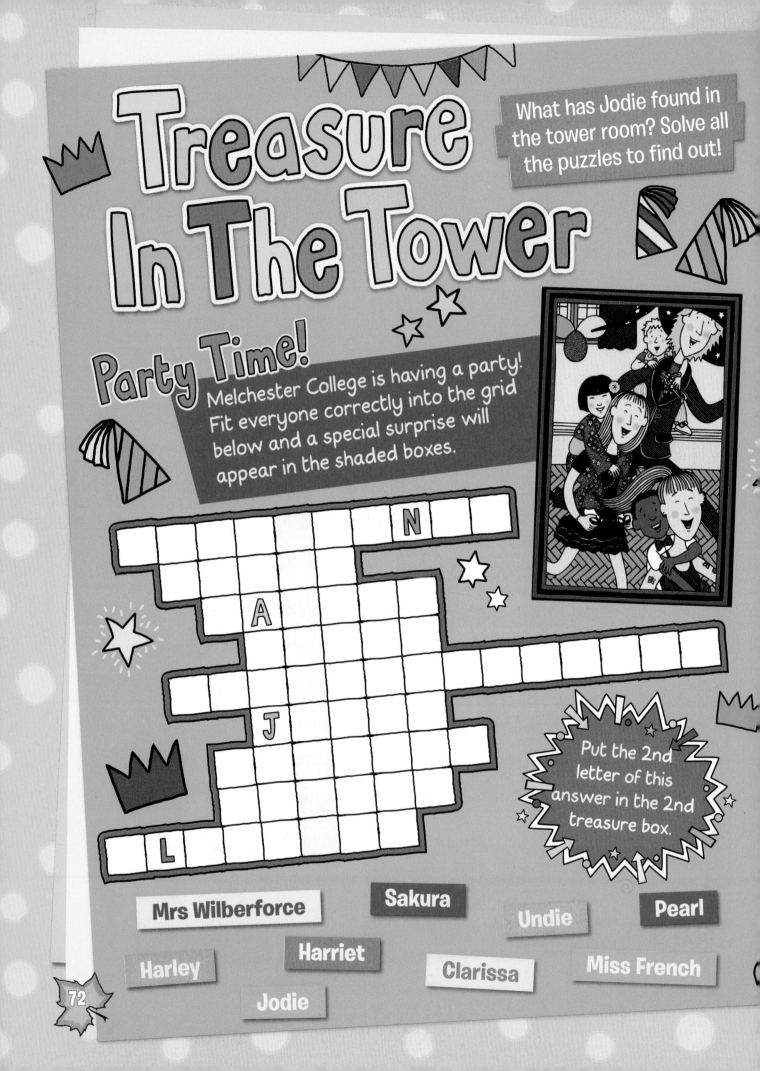

N

A

J

L

Put the 2nd letter of this answer in the 2nd treasure box.

Mrs Wilberforce   **Sakura**   **Undie**   **Pearl**

Harley   **Harriet**   **Clarissa**   **Miss French**

Jodie

Colour Crazy!

Jodie has dyed her hair a wacky colour — again!

Cross out the letters that appear three times and read the left-over letters to find out what colour she has picked.

K V S W A P R X B X
I P W O R B K R A S
X A L K E W S B T P

Jodie's hair is _ _ _ _ _ _

Put the 6th letter of this answer in the 1st treasure box.

Furry Friends

Fill in the missing letter on each line to make two new words. Pearl's favourite animal will appear in the shaded boxes.

THUM		OUNCE
DRAM		PPLE
BIR		RUM
FRO		OLF
CHEES		MPTY
FEA		OBIN

Put the **2nd letter** of this answer in the 5th treasure box.

Dear Diary...

Pearl has written about a special friend in her diary. Can you work out who it is?

I have so much in common with my new friend! We both love reading and animals — tonight we're sneaking out to watch the badgers! Perhaps this new school won't be so bad after all...

The friend is _ _ _ _ _ _

Put the 2nd letter of this answer in the 3rd treasure box. Put the 3rd letter of this answer in the 4th treasure box.

The secret treasure is a...

1 2 3 4 5

Super-scary Snacks!

SPOOKY COOKIES!

You'll need:

- Pack of plain cookies
- Butter icing or ready-made frosting
- Red food colouring
- Tic Tac sweets
- Fruit gums
- White icing tube
- Liquorice laces

1. Colour the frosting with a few drops of red colouring and spread on the bottoms of two cookies.

2. Put the fruit gum at the edge of one cookie and prop the other cookie on top to make an open Cookie Monster mouth.

3. Add some Tic Tac teeth.

4. Make eyes with two blobs of white icing and little snips of liquorice lace.

Eeeek!

CREEPY CUPCAKES!

You'll need:

- Plain cupcakes or mini muffins
- Chocolate butter icing or ready-made frosting
- Mini red Smarties or M&Ms
- White icing tube
- Liquorice laces

1. Cover a cupcake with the chocolate icing. Fluff it up with a fork for a spiky look.

2. Stick on some glowing Smartie or M&M eyes.

3. Stick some little snips of liquorice lace to the eyes with dabs of icing.

4. Dot on frightening fangs with the white icing tube.

5. Make eight creepy crawly spider legs for each cake with liquorice laces.

Aaarrrgh!

How to Make Butter Icing

You'll need:
- 140g butter or margarine
- 280g icing sugar
- 1 tablespoon cocoa powder (for chocolate flavour)
- A little milk

Makes enough to cover 12 cakes or cookies.

1. Beat the butter in a bowl to soften.
2. Sift in the icing sugar (and cocoa powder if you're making chocolate flavour).
3. Mix together till you get a smooth, spreadable frosting.
4. Add a little milk if the mix is too stiff to spread.

Always ask an adult before using any kitchen equipment.

Happily Ever After?

Write amazing endings and gripping conclusions!

1

What to do:

- Pick a word from one of the four corners.
- Count the letters in the word and open and close the Conclusion Chooser the same number of times.
- Now pick one of the numbers and open and close as you count it out.
- Choose a final number and lift the flap to find your fantastic finale!

Make It! 1. Cut out the Conclusion Chooser and turn it over so this side is face down.

2. Fold each corner into the centre to make a diamond shape.

3. Flip it over and fold the corners into the middle again.

4. Fold the square in half.

5. Put your thumbs and forefingers under each flap and push the four corners together to meet in the middle.

FINALE

1 — There's a mysterious knock at the door on the stroke of midnight. Who is at the door?

2 — The shock arrival of a long-lost enemy spoils a happy family gathering.

DILEMMA

3 — Someone spills a deep, dark secret that will change your characters' lives forever.

4 — Love is in the air! A true romance will blossom between two of your characters.

The strangest thing happens when an antique doll is found in the attic.

5

DRAMA

A one-way ticket to Australia lands on the doorstep. Will your character stay or go?

6

CRISIS

7 — Your character's mum buys a scratch card and wins the £5000 jackpot! What will they do with the money?

8 — A reunion with a loved one will be the happiest day of your character's life.

76

Nick Sharratt
AMAZING ILLUSTRATOR

Turn over for drawing and design heaven...

- ⭐ A–Z of Nick Sharratt
- ⭐ Design a new shirt for Nick
- ⭐ Create a best-selling book cover
- ⭐ Nick answers **your** questions
- ⭐ Peek at Nick's favourite festive decorations
- ⭐ Cut out a Destiny Diary
- ⭐ Design your own book labels

A-Z of Nick Sharratt

All you need to know!

Abba
Nick loves to listen to this group and pop music from the 70s.

Bexleyheath
Where Nick was born. Now he lives in *Brighton*.

Charlie and the Chocolate Factory
This book was one of his childhood favourites.

Design
He studied graphic design at St Martin's School of Art in London.

Easter Eggs
Nick used to design wrappers and packaging for these!

Friends and Family
Nick has a younger brother and two younger sisters. His best friend is Jon.

Gold Blue Peter Badge
He was awarded one of these in 2009.

Holidays
You might spot him camping in the Yorkshire Dales!

Illustrator
It's what Nick always wanted to be. He started painting when he was small.

Jacqueline Wilson
Nick and Jacky have worked together for over 20 years and are great friends.

Keyboard
Nick's computer keyboard is covered with grubby pencil marks!

78

Messy muddle
His art studio is very untidy!

Lucky number
37

Nicholas Joseph Sharratt
Nick's full name.

Orange juice
He loves it on his cornflakes!

Pasta and Pesto
Mmmm! It's one of his favourite foods.

Questions!
Nick is always asked what inspires him and what he'd be if he wasn't an illustrator.

Reading
He reads Jacky's books a few times before he starts drawing the characters.

Slippers
Nick always wears his favourite pair when he's working in his studio.

Tracy Beaker
The JW character he has drawn more times than any other.

Unique drawing style
Nick's bold, colourful and award-winning artwork stands out on the book shelves.

Vision On
His must-see TV show when he was young.

Woodsmoke
It's his favourite smell!

X-factor
Nick's definitely got it!

Yellow
Nick loves this colour, the brighter and sunnier the better!

Zzzz...
Illustrating over 200 books is tiring work!

79

Design a Shirt for Nick!

It's an awesome art challenge!

Nick loves to wear shirts with unusual or intricate patterns. Use all your artist skills to design a new one. Here are some helpful suggestions...

Will you be inspired by the sea with ocean creatures like sea horses, colourful fish, tiny crabs and starfish swimming across the fabric?

What about something really unusual like many different styles of hats?

Maybe you'll be influenced by the Victorians. Perhaps distinguished gentlemen with top hats, handlebar moustaches and Penny Farthing cycles?

Will you use a rainbow of coloured swirls and random designs?

Nick loves sweets! Why not create a shirt that's too good to eat?

Would Nick like a shirt inspired by a country? Imagine rich embroidered patterns, stars and stripes or world flag designs.

Why not add nature patterns like leaves and flowers? What about tiny little butterflies, an army of ants or a wiggle of worms?

What shape will the buttons be? You could use other fastenings like a colourful zip or gemstone studs.

Could you design a best-selling book cover?

Create A Cover!

A great book cover has to do lots of things such as:

- Stand out on the shop shelves
- Make you want to pick up the book and find out more
- Give you a sense of the story inside

Nick reads Jacky's stories over and over to think of clever ways of doing all this.
Look at these covers to see how —

Hetty is drawn in sepia brown to show that life at the Foundling Hospital is sparse and dull.

Jacqueline Wilson
HETTY FEATHER
ILLUSTRATED BY NICK SHARRATT
Will Hetty ever find her true home?

Matron Pig-face scowls at Hetty, but Hetty's expression is hopeful. She won't give up on returning to the real-world life she once knew.

The imposing hospital building wraps round Hetty like a prison, keeping her inside.

But exploding round Hetty are the bright colours of life outside and the excitement of the circus she remembers from her early years.

82

Hetty has grown up and left her drab brown Foundling life.

Nick has drawn her in bright colours with her hair flowing in the wind. She has a new name, Sapphire, but is she truly free now?

Jacqueline Wilson
SAPPHIRE BATTERSEA
ILLUSTRATED BY NICK SHARRATT
A new name, a new life for HETTY FEATHER

Has she moved to the seaside or is she just visiting?

Who are all the new characters in Sapphire's life? Pick up the book to find out!

Jacqueline Wilson

LITTLE DARLINGS

TWO VERY DIFFERENT GIRLS — ONE EXTRAORDINARY FRIENDSHIP!

ILLUSTRATED BY NICK SHARRATT

DESTINY

Nick has used a celebrity magazine format to tell the story of Destiny and Sunset, the daughters of rock star, Danny Kilman.

The tear down the centre shows that the two girls are living worlds apart.

The backgrounds emphasise this — Destiny is surrounded by an ordinary housing estate while Sunset walks the red carpet being snapped by photographers.

But Destiny looks happy and Sunset seems nervous, so what is the *real* story of their lives?

At first glance the cover for *Cookie* looks super-sweet with the pink colours, icing edging and cute biscuit shapes.

JACQUELINE WILSON

Cookie

Illustrated by Nick Sharratt

But the hand smashing the bunny cookie hints at something bad happening in Beauty Cookson's world. Are you desperate to find out what?

Jacqueline Wilson

★STARRING★ TRACY BEAKER

BRAND NEW NOVEL

...ated by Nick Sharra...

Nick has surrounded Tracy with a bright exploding star. The colours shoot out towards you showing that Tracy is definitely the centre of attention.

Jacqueline Wilso...

Lily Alo...

BRAND NEW BEST-SELLER

Sometimes Lily wishes she really was home ALONE

Illustrated by Nick Sharratt

Lily Alone is similar in that Lily is also in the centre surrounded by a shape. But this time it's a dark circle and Lily looks lost inside.

Turn over for more!

Take the Cover Test!

Are you the next
Nick Sharratt?

On the cover of *Best Friends*, Nick
has drawn a busy, winding road
between Alice and Gemma. This is
a perfect way to illustrate the
distance between the
two besties.

Jacqueline Wilson

Best
Friends

Alice
and
Gemma

Illustrated by Nick Sharratt

Your challenge is to create
a brand new *Best Friends*
cover. Think of a new way
to show that the BFs have
been torn apart and
separated by miles.

On your cover you must include
Alice and Gemma, the name of the
book and Jacky's name

Tip!
Jacqueline Wilson is always clearly
written across the top of JW books.
This makes them instantly recognisable
amongst the other authors.

Design a bright, stand-out logo for your mag title.

Pick your best fun features to highlight alongside your cover star.

I'll help you create a cover.

A simple, easy to read cover look will make each item really pop!

What's the idea of your mag? A tagline says it all in one snappy Teatment.

Cover Must-haves!

Tick them off as you go —

- **Title**
- **Tagline**
- **Gifts** — will you include special gifts?
- **Cover stars** — the main feature of your magazine
- **Competitions** — any fabulous prizes on offer?
- **Features** — make your mag sound amazing!

Get your pens and paper and start drawing!

Nick's Super Secrets!

Your questions answered!

When you are given a name of a person or character, can you instantly make up in your mind what you think they might look like?
HANNAH, EPSOM

Sometimes I can, if they are called something intriguing like Mrs Briskett in *Sapphire Battersea* or Sunset in *Little Darlings*, but for less unusual names I need a few more clues, which I'm always able to find by the time I've read the whole manuscript.

SKETCH BOOK

I am an artist like you! I only feel spontaneous when a picture or object inspires me. Is there something or someone who inspires you?
SADIA, SOLIHULL

Well, Jacqueline's stories are always inspiring, but I'm also motivated by the fact I have a job to do, and I'd be in big trouble if I couldn't think anything to draw!

Hi, Nick! If you were king for a day, what would you do?
ROBYN, GLASGOW

I'm going to sound like a grumpy old man but I would ban all idle chat on mobile phones in public places like trains, cafés and shops for my day — it drives me nuts!

How much chocolate do you eat in a day?
EMILY, NORTHANTS

I'm now trying to limit myself to two small pieces a day, but I have a really big supply in my cupboard so it's taking an awful lot of will power!

Sweets

If the world ended in 2013 what three things would you save?
MIA, BIRMINGHAM

Gosh, I hope it doesn't, but I'd save the drawings I did when I was very young, my computer because it's got so many photos on it, and for particular sentimental reasons, a ceramic tile I have with a picture of a lion on it.

How does it feel when you wake up in the morning and know you get to do something you love every day?
IBBY, DURSLEY

I feel extremely lucky. And sometimes I find myself waking up extra-early because I just can't wait to get up and start work!

I'm the greatest!

Which of Jacqueline Wilson's books is your favourite and why?
RACHEL, COBH

The Story of Tracy Beaker will always be my favourite I think, but I'm very fond of *Double Act* and *The Lottie Project* too.

What is your favourite art gallery to visit?
GEORGIE, CHATHAM

I have two galleries that I always look forward to visiting because their exhibitions are so good: the Scottish National Gallery of Modern Art in Edinburgh and Pallant House in Chichester.

Merry Nick-mas!

Nick's tree is a work of art!

All my Christmas decorations are second-hand and most of them are quite old and fragile. It's wonderful how they have lasted through the years.

I came across the blue-eyed fairy in her original box and she must be about 70 years old. Her wings were missing so I made her some new ones from tracing paper.

I really like old fashioned hand decorated baubles and it's amazing what great things you can find at flea markets and car boot sales.

My favourites are these groovy spik plastic decoration. I think they must come from the 1960s.

I have lots of very old paper lanterns, bells and bunting too. I use them to decorate the house and my studio.

I like a real tree though one year I had a neon pink inflatable tree just for a change!

These tiny crackers are much too nice to pull!

I always design my own Christmas card.

Destiny Diary

Your own mini planner and lucky charms for 2013!

Discover your lucky number, charms and colour for every month!

Cut out and keep for the year ahead!

January

....

....

Special Dates:

....

....

Luck: 5

February

....

Special Dates:

....

....

Luck: 1

March

....

....

Special Dates:

....

....

Luck: 8

April

....

....

Special Dates:

....

....

Luck: 3

May

....

....

Special Dates:

....

....

Luck: 2

June

....

....

Special Dates:

....

....

Luck: 10

July

....
....

Special Dates:

....
....

Luck: 4

August

....
....

Special Dates:

....
....

Luck: 6

September

....
....

Special Dates:

....
....

Luck: 11

October

....
....

Special Dates:

....
....

Luck: 7

November

....
....

Special Dates:

....
....

Luck: 12

December

....
....

Special Dates:

....
....

Luck: 9

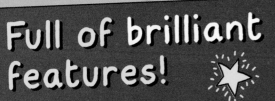

The Official Jacqueline Wilson Mag™

Full of brilliant features!

- ✓ Exclusive writing tips from Jacqueline Wilson
- ✓ Draw with Nick Sharratt
- ✓ Fun flowcharts and puzzles
- ✓ A letter from Jacqueline Wilson in every issue
- ✓ Exclusive sneak preview stories
- ✓ Learn all about Jacky's brilliant books

ONLY £5 for three months by direct debit*

Never miss an issue

POSTAGE IS FREE!

HOW TO GET THIS OFFER:

Ask an adult to —

Log on to www.jw-mag.com/subs

Call free on **0800 318 846**
(Freephone from UK landlines only)

Pay by direct debit and SAVE £20!

Please quote **JWANO** when ordering

*£5 for first quarter and £10 per quarter thereafter by direct Debit.
** £20 saving based on Direct Debit offer price compared to non-direct price.
Non-direct Debit price: One year £55 (UK), 6 months £30 (UK).
Overseas rates available on application. Offer ends 5th January 2014.

sweeties
yum!

Baby Tracy

poster paints

dream house